Maths
Progress Papers 1

Patrick Berry

Schofield&Sims

Introduction

The **Maths Progress Papers** provide structured activities that increase in difficulty throughout the series, developing your knowledge and skills in maths. Use the books to prepare for school entrance examinations and to improve your maths skills.

How to use this book

There are seven papers in this book. Each contains 100 questions, divided by topic into sets of five. A single paper may take between 45 and 75 minutes to complete, and you might need two or more sessions to complete one paper.

- For exam preparation, revision and all-round practice, you may choose to work through the papers in numerical order. Once you have completed a paper, ask a teacher, parent or adult helper to correct any mistakes and to explain where you went wrong.

- To practise a topic that you find particularly challenging, work through selected activities in order of difficulty using the **Topics chart**, available to download from the Schofield & Sims website.

Each question should be answered without using a calculator. You may use a separate piece of paper to work out the answers to any questions that require more complex calculations.

Answers

The answers to all the questions in this book can be found in a pull-out section in the middle. You (or an adult) should use this to mark your work at the end of each paper. You will receive one mark for each correct answer, giving you a total mark out of 100 for every paper. Take time to learn and remember why the answer given is correct.

Use the **Progress Chart** at the back of this book to record your marks and measure progress.

Downloads

Free downloads are available from the Schofield & Sims website (www.schofieldandsims.co.uk/free-downloads), including extra practice material.

Published by **Schofield & Sims Ltd**,
7 Mariner Court, Wakefield, West Yorkshire WF4 3FL, UK
Telephone 01484 607080
www.schofieldandsims.co.uk

First published in 1994
This edition copyright © Schofield & Sims, 2018
Fifth impression 2022

Author: **Patrick Berry**
Revised by Rebecca Brant and Peter Hall
Patrick Berry has asserted his moral rights under the Copyright, Designs and Patents Act, 1988, to be identified as the author of this work.

British Library Cataloguing in Publication Data
A catalogue record for this book is available from the British Library.

Design by **Ledgard Jepson Ltd**

Printed in the UK by **Page Bros (Norwich) Ltd**

ISBN 978 07217 1456 1

Contents

Note for parents, tutors, teachers and other adult helpers

A pull-out answers section (pages A1 to A12) appears in the centre of this book, between pages 24 and 25 (Paper 4). This provides answers to all the questions, along with guidance on marking the papers. Remove the pull-out section before the child begins working through the practice papers.

Q. 1–5

simple addition and subtraction

1	2	3	4	5
34 + 25	584 + 378	5988 + 3769	43 − 27	532 − 146

1 ☐
2 ☐
3 ☐
4 ☐
5 ☐

Q. 6–10

pie charts

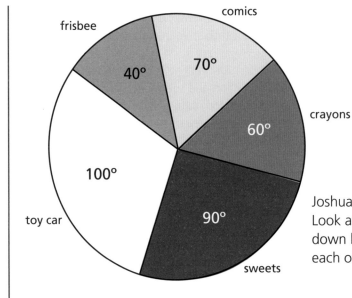

Joshua spends £3.60 in town. Look at the pie chart and write down how much he spends on each of the following.

6	sweets	_____ p	6 ☐
7	toy car	_____ p	7 ☐
8	crayons	_____ p	8 ☐
9	frisbee	_____ p	9 ☐
10	comics	_____ p	10 ☐

Q. 11–15

simple multiplication

11	12	13	14	15
9 × 12	25 × 8	200 × 6	783 × 11	668 × 9

11 ☐
12 ☐
13 ☐
14 ☐
15 ☐

Q. 16–20

simple division

16	17	18	19	20
4)128	6)960	8)672	9)846	12)6792

16 ☐
17 ☐
18 ☐
19 ☐
20 ☐

MARK ☐

MARK
✓ or ✗

Q. 21–25

addition and subtraction problems

21 Add together seventeen and fourteen. _____ | 21 ☐

22 How many is six hundred and twelve plus ninety-nine? _____ | 22 ☐

23 What is six hundred and two minus three hundred and fifteen? _____ | 23 ☐

24 To five thousand and twenty add the sum of eighteen and twelve. _____ | 24 ☐

25 A farmer had eighty-seven cows, one hundred and sixty-three sheep, fifteen goats and thirty-nine horses. How many animals did he have altogether? Write your answer in words.

_____ | 25 ☐

Q. 26–30

multiplication problems

26 Multiply seven hundred and thirty-six by seven. _____ | 26 ☐

27 What is the product of ninety-six and twelve? _____ | 27 ☐

28 What is seven thousand six hundred and eighty-eight times five? _____ | 28 ☐

29 Write down the product of seventy-seven and seven. _____ | 29 ☐

30 How many is twelve times sixteen thousand four hundred and ninety-three? _____ | 30 ☐

Q. 31–35

division problems

31 What is eight hundred and eighty-eight divided by three? _____ | 31 ☐

32 Divide ninety-six by four. _____ | 32 ☐

33 If 392 chocolate buttons are shared among 8 children, how many does each child get? _____ | 33 ☐

34 What is two thousand eight hundred and eighty-four divided by seven? _____ | 34 ☐

35 Divide sixty-two stickers between a pair of children. How many stickers does each child get? _____ | 35 ☐

Q. 36–40

decimal addition and subtraction

36
$$\begin{array}{r} 6.4 \\ +\ 3.8 \\ \hline \end{array}$$

37
$$\begin{array}{r} 17.46 \\ 8.37 \\ +\ 5.98 \\ \hline \end{array}$$

38
$$\begin{array}{r} 66.09 \\ 3.76 \\ +\ 100.48 \\ \hline \end{array}$$

39
$$\begin{array}{r} 7.06 \\ 6.09 \\ 8.58 \\ +\ 12.87 \\ \hline \end{array}$$

40
$$\begin{array}{r} 13.04 \\ -\ 11.95 \\ \hline \end{array}$$

36 ☐
37 ☐
38 ☐
39 ☐
40 ☐

MARK ☐

Q. 41–45

timetables

Bus timetable: Flockton – Lepton

Flockton Dep.	Emley Arr.	Emley Dep.	Lepton Arr.
08.30	08.55	09.15	10.10
11.20	11.45	12.10	13.05
16.05	16.30	16.32	17.27

41 How long does the 08.30 bus from Flockton take to get to Lepton? _____ h _____ min   **41** ☐

42 How many minutes longer does the 11.20 bus take? _____ min   **42** ☐

43 How many minutes does the 11.20 bus wait at Emley? _____ min   **43** ☐

44 If I miss the 08.30 bus from Flockton by 20 minutes, how long will I wait for the next bus? _____ h _____ min   **44** ☐

45 How long does the last bus take to complete the journey? _____ h _____ min   **45** ☐

Q. 46–50

symmetry

Draw a line of symmetry through each of these shapes.

46 ☐
47 ☐
48 ☐
49 ☐
50 ☐

46

47

48

49

50

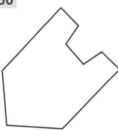

Q. 51–55

decimal problems

51 How many pence are there in 0.7 of £1.00? _____ p   **51** ☐

52 How many minutes are there in 0.1 of one hour? _____ min   **52** ☐

53 How much is 0.2 of fifty pence? _____ p   **53** ☐

54 What decimal fraction of 50 tonnes is 10 tonnes? _____   **54** ☐

55 Add 20.63 and 57.48 and subtract the result from one hundred. _____   **55** ☐

MARK ☐

MARK
✓ or ✗

Q. 56–60

reduce to lowest terms

56 Reduce $\frac{8}{16}$ to its lowest terms. _____ | 56 ☐

57 Reduce $\frac{7}{14}$ to its lowest terms. _____ | 57 ☐

58 Express $\frac{15}{40}$ in its lowest terms. _____ | 58 ☐

59 Write the improper fraction $\frac{14}{5}$ as a mixed number in its lowest terms. _____ | 59 ☐

60 Write down $4\frac{3}{8}$ as an improper fraction. _____ | 60 ☐

Q. 61–65

fraction addition and subtraction

61

$\frac{1}{7} + \frac{5}{7} =$ _____

62

$\frac{2}{5} + \frac{1}{10} =$ _____

63

$\frac{2}{3} + \frac{1}{4} =$ _____

| 61 ☐
| 62 ☐
| 63 ☐

64

$\frac{11}{12} - \frac{2}{3} =$ _____

65

$\frac{11}{15} - \frac{1}{3} =$ _____

| 64 ☐
| 65 ☐

Q. 66–70

fraction problems

66 If $\frac{2}{3}$ of Ben's room is painted blue and $\frac{1}{6}$ is painted red, what fraction of his room is painted? _____ | 66 ☐

67 What fraction of a week is three days? _____ | 67 ☐

68 One quarter of a number is 17. What is the number? _____ | 68 ☐

69 $\frac{11}{16}$ of the children in a class are boys. What fraction are girls? _____ | 69 ☐

70 Write down the largest of these fractions.
$\frac{3}{4} \quad \frac{3}{6} \quad \frac{3}{8} \quad \frac{3}{10} \quad \frac{3}{12}$ _____ | 70 ☐

Q. 71–75

percentage problems

71 Express 8 as a percentage of 16. _____% | 71 ☐

72 Express 8 as a percentage of 32. _____% | 72 ☐

73 A shopkeeper sold 36 cakes from her stock of 48. What percentage did she sell? _____% | 73 ☐

74 How much is 64% of a hundred? _____ | 74 ☐

75 What percentage is 3 pence of 15 pence? _____% | 75 ☐

MARK ☐

MARK
✓ or ✗

Q. 76–80

Venn
diagrams

This diagram shows how pupils in Year 5 travel to school.

Each **X** in the diagram represents one pupil.

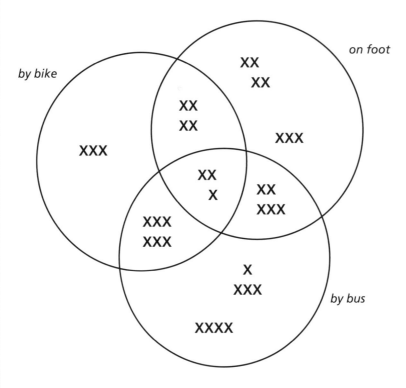

76 How many pupils only use one mode of transport? _____ 76 ☐

77 How many use two modes of transport? _____ 77 ☐

78 How many use all three modes of transport? _____ 78 ☐

79 How many travel on foot? _____ 79 ☐

80 How many travel by bike? _____ 80 ☐

Q. 81–85

money
problems

81 To £26.26 add £62.62. £ _____ 81 ☐

82 Add together 60 pence, £60.00 and sixty ten pence pieces. £ _____ 82 ☐

83 Add a quarter of a pound to a fifth of a pound and write
the answer in pounds and pence. £ _____ 83 ☐

84 Add 1716p, 54p, 168p and 377p.
Give the answer in pounds and pence. £ _____ 84 ☐

85 Find the difference between £18.02 and £3.98. £ _____ 85 ☐

MARK ☐

MARK
✓ or ✗

9

Q. 86–90

prime
numbers

This is a method of discovering the prime numbers between 1 and 100 using the Sieve of Eratosthenes.

One mark will be given for each of the five tasks below.

1	2	3	4	5	6	7	8	9	10
11	12	13	14	15	16	17	18	19	20
21	22	23	24	25	26	27	28	29	30
31	32	33	34	35	36	37	38	39	40
41	42	43	44	45	46	47	48	49	50
51	52	53	54	55	56	57	58	59	60
61	62	63	64	65	66	67	68	69	70
71	72	73	74	75	76	77	78	79	80
81	82	83	84	85	86	87	88	89	90
91	92	93	94	95	96	97	98	99	100

On the chart above:

86 Cross out 1, which isn't a prime number. Cross out all the numbers which can be divided by 2, except 2 itself.

86 ☐

87 Cross out all the numbers which can be divided by 3, except 3 itself.

87 ☐

88 Cross out all the numbers which can be divided by 5, except 5 itself.

88 ☐

89 Cross out all the numbers which can be divided by 7, except 7 itself.

89 ☐

90 You are left with the prime numbers between 1 and 100.
How many are there? _____

90 ☐

MARK ☐

MARK
✓ or ✗

Q. 91–95

measures addition and subtraction

91

£ . p
17.06
9.37
+ 10.53
_____

92

kg g
426 100
152 007
+ 39 916
_____

93

Measure and add together the four lengths above.
Write your answer in cm and mm.

_____ cm _____ mm

94 12 hours 40 mins − 3 hours 54 mins = _____ h _____ min

95 6.005 litres − 2.75 litres = _____ l

91	
92	
93	
94	
95	

Q. 96–100

pictograms

This is a simple pictogram where each stick figure represents one person.
The pictogram shows what a set of people prefer for breakfast.

toast	🧍🧍🧍🧍🧍🧍🧍🧍🧍🧍🧍
cereal	🧍🧍🧍🧍🧍🧍🧍🧍🧍
porridge	🧍🧍🧍🧍🧍🧍🧍🧍🧍🧍🧍🧍🧍🧍🧍
fruit	🧍🧍🧍🧍🧍🧍🧍🧍🧍🧍
cooked breakfast	🧍🧍🧍🧍🧍

96 How many people were asked what they preferred? _____

97 What fraction of the group preferred fruit? _____

98 What fraction preferred porridge? _____

99 What decimal fraction of the group preferred a cooked breakfast? _____

100 What percentage of the group preferred either toast or cereal? _____%

96	
97	
98	
99	
100	

END OF TEST

PAPER 1 TOTAL MARK [ ]

Paper 2

MARK
✓ or ✗

Q. 1–5

writing large numbers

Write down in words the number represented by each diagram.

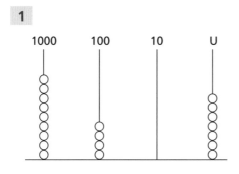

1

1000   100   10   U

_____

_____

2

1000   100   10   U

_____

_____

3

10 000   1000   100   10   U

_____

_____

4

10 000   1000   100   10   U

_____

_____

5

10 000
1000
100
10
U

_____

_____

1	☐
2	☐
3	☐
4	☐
5	☐

Q. 6–10

large number problems

6 Add six hundred and seventy to one hundred and ninety. _____

7 Subtract five thousand two hundred from nine thousand. _____

8 Multiply fourteen thousand and twenty by six. _____

9 Divide twenty-eight thousand and two by three. _____

10 Three thousand two hundred people live in Framlingham and seven thousand one hundred and six people live in Woodbridge. How many more people live in Woodbridge than in Framlingham? _____

6	☐
7	☐
8	☐
9	☐
10	☐

MARK ☐

MARK
✓ or ✗

Q. 11–15

long multiplication

11	12	13	14
28 × 15	67 × 26	89 × 47	35 × 92

15 163 × 48 = _____

11	
12	
13	
14	
15	

Q. 16–20

decimal multiplication

16 7.4 × 10 = _____

17 8.6 × 10 = _____

18 5.06 × 10 = _____

19 24.73 × 10 = _____

20 0.384 × 10 = _____

16	
17	
18	
19	
20	

Q. 21–25

decimal division

21 7.4 ÷ 10 = _____

22 8.6 ÷ 10 = _____

23 5.06 ÷ 10 = _____

24 24.73 ÷ 10 = _____

25 0.384 ÷ 10 = _____

21	
22	
23	
24	
25	

Q. 26–30

decimal problems

26 Add 0.5 of 50p to 0.4 of £1. _____ p

27 Subtract 0.5 of an hour from 0.7 of an hour and write the answer in minutes. _____ min

28 Write in hours 0.75 of a day. _____ h

29 Take 12p from 0.62 of £1. _____ p

30 What is 0.7 of seventy kilometres? _____ km

26	
27	
28	
29	
30	

Q. 31–35

fraction multiplication and division

31 $\frac{2}{9} \times \frac{3}{8} =$ _____

32 $\frac{5}{6} \div 5 =$ _____

33 $\frac{4}{9} \div 8 =$ _____

34 $\frac{4}{33}$ of $\frac{11}{12} =$ _____

35 $\frac{3}{8}$ of $\frac{16}{21} =$ _____

31	
32	
33	
34	
35	

MARK [ ]

MARK
✓ or ✗

Q. 36–40

coordinates

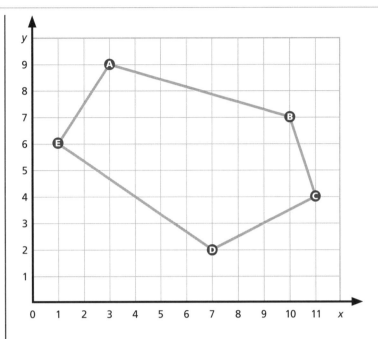

| 36 |
| 37 |
| 38 |
| 39 |
| 40 |

Write down the coordinates of the corners of this shape.
(Remember: along the x axis, then up the y axis.)

36	37	38	39	40

A = ___ , ___   B = ___ , ___   C = ___ , ___   D = ___ , ___   E = ___ , ___

Q. 41–45

fraction
problems

41 What fraction of a circle is 120 degrees? _____ | 41 |

42 Add $\frac{2}{3}$ of 12 to $\frac{3}{8}$ of 16. _____ | 42 |

43 What fraction of 1 hour is 24 minutes? _____ | 43 |

44 An 800ml bottle is $\frac{3}{4}$ full.
How many ml does it contain? _____ ml | 44 |

45 A fifth of a sum of money is £3.50.
How much is the full amount? £ _____ | 45 |

Q. 46–50

fractions to
percentages

Write down the shaded fraction of each circle as a percentage.

46 **47** **48** **49** **50**

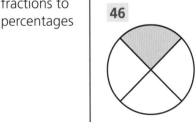 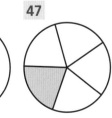 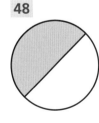 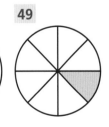 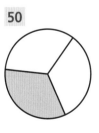

_____ % _____ % _____ % _____ % _____ %

| 46 |
| 47 |
| 48 |
| 49 |
| 50 |

MARK

MARK
✓ or ✗

Q. 51–55

measures multiplication and division

51	£.p	52	kg g	53	l ml
	24.48		7 063		86 427
	× 4		× 5		× 6

51 ☐
52 ☐
53 ☐

54 7 km 545m ÷ 5 = _____ km _____ m

54 ☐

55 3 days ÷ 4 = _____ h

55 ☐

Q. 56–60

factors and multiples

56 List all the factors of 12. _____ 56 ☐

57 List all the factors of 36. _____ 57 ☐

58 List all the factors of 48. _____ 58 ☐

59 List the first 5 multiples of 14. _____ 59 ☐

60 List the first 5 multiples of 17. _____ 60 ☐

Q. 61–65

money problems

61 If I save £7.50 each week for nine weeks, how much will I have at the end of that time? £ _____ 61 ☐

62 If potatoes cost 20p per kg, how much will a sack weighing 25kg cost? £ _____ 62 ☐

63 What is the cost of 4 beanbags at £35.75 each? £ _____ 63 ☐

64 If you share the sum of £16.20 and £70.68 equally among twelve people, how much does each get? £ _____ 64 ☐

65 The lottery jackpot was one million pounds. Five people shared it. How much did each win? £ _____ 65 ☐

Q. 66–70

shape properties

Match the names to the 2-D shapes below.

kite	trapezium	parallelogram	square	rhombus

66   67   68   69   70

66 ☐
67 ☐
68 ☐
69 ☐
70 ☐

_____ _____ _____ _____ _____

MARK ☐

MARK
✓ or ✗

Q. 71–75

24-hour clock

Change these a.m. and p.m. times to 24-hour clock times.

71 **72** **73** **74** **75**

a.m.   p.m.   p.m.   p.m.   p.m.

_____ _____ _____ _____ _____

71	
72	
73	
74	
75	

Q. 76–80

BODMAS

76 $(3 \times 6) + 7 =$ _____

77 $6(4 + 5) =$ _____

78 $(2 \times 5) + (4 \times 12) =$ _____

79 $(5 - 2) + 4^2 =$ _____

80 $48 \div (4 \times 2) - 2^2 =$ _____

76	
77	
78	
79	
80	

Q. 81–85

what is my number?

81 One third of my number, doubled is 16.
What is my number? _____

82 I think of a number, divide it by seven and add 15.
The answer is 23. What is my number? _____

83 I think of a number, add 19 and multiply by 4.
The answer is 92. What is my number? _____

84 One fifth of my number, add 7 is 14.
What is my number? _____

85 I think of a number, multiply it by 8 then subtract 18.
The answer is 30. What is my number? _____

81	
82	
83	
84	
85	

Q. 86–90

greater, equals and less than

Use the signs <, >, or = to make each sentence true.

86 4×6 _____ 5×5

87 17×4 _____ 7×9

88 $\frac{2}{3}$ _____ $\frac{4}{5}$

89 $\frac{6}{10}$ _____ $\frac{15}{25}$

90 6.4 _____ $6\frac{1}{5}$

86	
87	
88	
89	
90	

MARK [   ]

MARK
✓ or ✗

Q. 91–95

reflection and rotation

Draw the reflections of the following shapes. Look carefully at the position of the mirror lines.

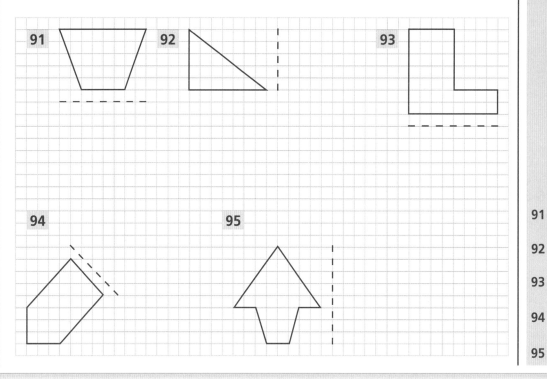

91	☐
92	☐
93	☐
94	☐
95	☐

Q. 96–100

Venn diagrams

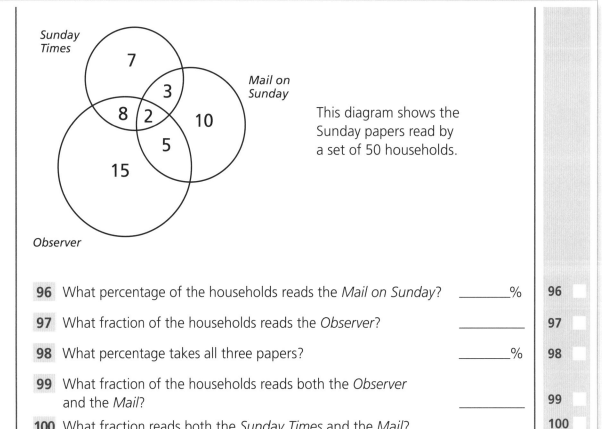

This diagram shows the Sunday papers read by a set of 50 households.

96 What percentage of the households reads the *Mail on Sunday*? _____% 96 ☐

97 What fraction of the households reads the *Observer*? _____ 97 ☐

98 What percentage takes all three papers? _____% 98 ☐

99 What fraction of the households reads both the *Observer* and the *Mail*? _____ 99 ☐

100 What fraction reads both the *Sunday Times* and the *Mail*? _____ 100 ☐

END OF TEST

PAPER 2 TOTAL MARK ☐

Paper 3

MARK
✓ or ✗

Q. 1–5
missing numbers

1
```
  2 4 □ 6
+ □ 9 5 □
  4 □ 3 2
```

2
```
  □ 8 9 □
+ 2 □ 5 8
  6 9 □ 4
```

3
```
  3 □ 8 5
- □ 4 5 □
  2 3 □ 1
```

4
```
    □ 7 5
  ×     6
  1 6 □ 0
```

5
```
      □ 8 4
  7)1 2 8 □
```

1	☐
2	☐
3	☐
4	☐
5	☐

Q. 6–10
long multiplication

6
```
  463
× 19
```

7
```
  859
× 25
```

8
```
  748
× 36
```

9
```
  3608
×   47
```

10 What is 6245 multiplied by 42?

6	☐
7	☐
8	☐
9	☐
10	☐

Q. 11–15
decimal multiplication

11 7.6 × 20 = _____

12 8.52 × 20 = _____

13 0.48 × 20 = _____

14 7.64 × 30 = _____

15 8.73 × 40 = _____

11	☐
12	☐
13	☐
14	☐
15	☐

Q. 16–20
decimal division

16 5.62 ÷ 10 = _____

17 5.62 ÷ 100 = _____

18 245.3 ÷ 1000 = _____

19 6.48 ÷ 20 = _____

20 6 ÷ 10 = _____

16	☐
17	☐
18	☐
19	☐
20	☐

Q. 21–25
reduce to lowest terms

Reduce these fractions to their simplest terms.

21 $\frac{24}{50}$ = _____

22 $\frac{21}{39}$ = _____

23 $\frac{33}{121}$ = _____

24 $\frac{24}{156}$ = _____

25 $\frac{45}{100}$ = _____

21	☐
22	☐
23	☐
24	☐
25	☐

MARK ☐

MARK
✓ or ✗

Q. 26–30

fraction addition and subtraction

26

$3\frac{3}{4} + 1\frac{1}{2} =$ _____

27

$1\frac{1}{3} + 2\frac{5}{6} =$ _____

28

$4\frac{3}{20} + 5\frac{3}{5} =$ _____

29

$\frac{2}{3} + \frac{5}{12} + \frac{3}{4} =$ _____

30

$3\frac{11}{12} - 2\frac{1}{2} =$ _____

26	☐
27	☐
28	☐
29	☐
30	☐

Q. 31–35

Venn diagrams

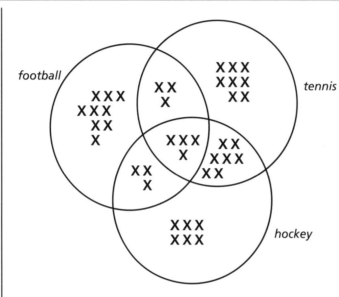

This diagram shows the sports played by a set of 40 children.

Each **X** in the diagram represents one child.

31 What fraction of the set plays hockey? _____

32 What fraction of the set plays tennis? _____

33 What fraction of the set plays both tennis and football? _____

34 What fraction of the set plays tennis only? _____

35 What fraction of the set plays all three sports? _____

31	☐
32	☐
33	☐
34	☐
35	☐

Q. 36–40

divisibility rules

36 Circle the numbers which are divisible by both 9 and 5.
324 135 450 213 90

37 Circle the numbers which are divisible by both 10 and 3.
200 60 123 420 120

38 Circle the numbers which are divisible by both 4 and 2.
214 528 360 487 796

Use your knowledge of divisibility rules to complete the following sums.

39 ___ × ___ × ___ = 315

40 ___ × ___ × ___ = 297

36	☐
37	☐
38	☐
39	☐
40	☐

MARK ☐

MARK
✓ or ✗

Q. 41–45

coordinates

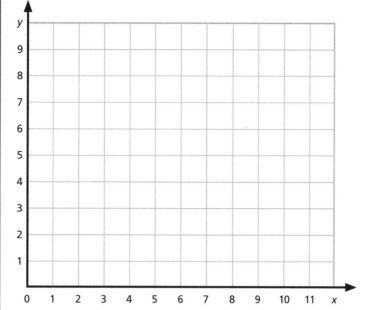

Below are the coordinates of five points, A, B, C, D and E.
Plot them on the squared grid and label each one with the correct letter.

41	42	43	44	45
A = 2, 8	B = 10, 9	C = 11, 2	D = 8, 5	E = 4, 4

41 ☐
42 ☐
43 ☐
44 ☐
45 ☐

Q. 46–50

long division

46	47	48	49	50
25)475	20)780	15)4590	21)798	35)1645

46 ☐
47 ☐
48 ☐
49 ☐
50 ☐

Q. 51–55

ratio and proportion

51 Alfie has six times as many stickers as Lucy.
Lucy has eight stickers. How many does Alfie have? _____

51 ☐

52 A shop sells 9 times as many red bags as brown bags.
If 63 red bags are sold, how many brown bags are sold? _____

52 ☐

53 Two in every seven children asked preferred salt and vinegar
crisps. If 56 children were asked, how many preferred
salt and vinegar? _____

53 ☐

54 There are 60 passengers on a bus. Seven in every 12 sit
downstairs. How many sit upstairs? _____

54 ☐

55 In a netball match, the home team scored 3 goals for every
2 goals scored by the away team. If a total of 30 goals
were scored, how many did the home team score? _____

55 ☐

MARK ☐

MARK
✓ or ✗

Q. 56–60

fraction multiplication and division

56

$1\frac{1}{6} \times 9 =$ _____

57

$8 \times 4\frac{1}{4} =$ _____

58

$\frac{4}{9} \times 3 =$ _____

59

$3 \div \frac{1}{3} =$ _____

60

$2\frac{1}{2} \div \frac{1}{2} =$ _____

56	☐
57	☐
58	☐
59	☐
60	☐

Q. 61–65

using money

Work out the total for each line. Then check that they all add up to the total given.

Thomson's Corner Stores
Jubilee Road

£ . p

61   3 apples at 35p each   =

62   7 onions each at 22p   =

63   24 eggs at 11p an egg   =

64   4 sweets at 27p each   =

65   6 doughnuts at 19p each   =

_____

Total =   7 . 4 5

_____

61	☐
62	☐
63	☐
64	☐
65	☐

Q. 66–70

area of shapes

Using the formula: area = $\frac{\text{base} \times \text{height}}{2}$, work out the area of the triangles below.

66

6cm

5cm

_____ cm²

67

4cm

8cm

_____ cm²

68

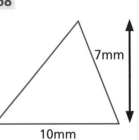

7mm

10mm

_____ mm²

69

6mm

11mm

_____ mm²

70

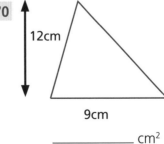

12cm

9cm

_____ cm²

66	☐
67	☐
68	☐
69	☐
70	☐

MARK ☐

MARK
✓ or ✗

Q. 71–75

graphs

This is a line graph showing the price of apples.

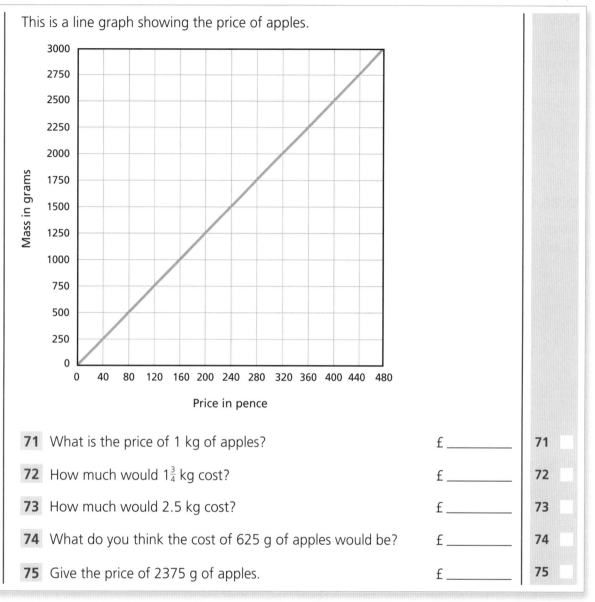

Price in pence

71	What is the price of 1 kg of apples?	£ _____	71 ☐
72	How much would $1\frac{3}{4}$ kg cost?	£ _____	72 ☐
73	How much would 2.5 kg cost?	£ _____	73 ☐
74	What do you think the cost of 625 g of apples would be?	£ _____	74 ☐
75	Give the price of 2375 g of apples.	£ _____	75 ☐

Q. 76–80

currency conversion

Use the currency conversion table below to answer the following questions.

Pound sterling	Euro	US dollar	Yen	Indian rupee
£1	€1.2	$1.5	¥150	₹90

76	How many yen would you get for £12?	¥ _____	76 ☐
77	What is $81 worth in £?	£ _____	77 ☐
78	If I had $90, how many yen could I buy?	¥ _____	78 ☐
79	I have ₹6300. How many euros could I buy with this?	€ _____	79 ☐
80	Which is greater in value, £55 or €65?	_____	80 ☐

MARK ☐

MARK
✓ or ✗

Q. 81–85

factors and multiples

81 What is the highest common factor of 18 and 42? _____ | 81 ☐

82 What is the highest common factor of 54 and 36? _____ | 82 ☐

83 What is the highest common factor of 42 and 70? _____ | 83 ☐

84 What is the lowest common multiple of 6 and 8? _____ | 84 ☐

85 What is the lowest common multiple of 12 and 36? _____ | 85 ☐

Q. 86–90

length problems

86 The perimeter of a play area is 40 metres.
If the play area is 8 metres wide, how long is it? _____ m | 86 ☐

87 If telegraph poles are placed 100 metres apart,
how many are needed to cover one kilometre? _____ | 87 ☐

88 Add $\frac{4}{5}$ of a kilometre to 3050 metres. _____ km _____ m | 88 ☐

89 If I run 3 km each day in order to keep fit,
how far will I run in total in May and June? _____ km | 89 ☐

90 A marathon is 42 km 195 m long.
If 12 people complete the race, what is
the total distance covered by them all? _____ km _____ m | 90 ☐

Q. 91–95

estimation and approximation

Estimate the answers to these questions by approximating. Underline the answer.
Do not try to work out the exact answer.

91 $297 \times 22 =$ 5500   6000   7000   4000   5000 | 91 ☐

92 $408 \times 97 =$ 40 000   37 500   43 000   38 000   42 000 | 92 ☐

93 $3506 \div 74 =$ 35   40   38   50   52 | 93 ☐

94 $246 \div 42 =$ 4   5   6   7   8 | 94 ☐

95 $194 \times 62 =$ 11 000   14 000   13 000   12 000   10 000 | 95 ☐

Q. 96–100

algebra

96 If $x + 4 = 9$, then $x =$ _____ | 96 ☐

97 If $8 = b - 5$, then $b =$ _____ | 97 ☐

98 If $4 \times q = 24$, then $q =$ _____ | 98 ☐

99 If $m + 7 = 38$, then $m =$ _____ | 99 ☐

100 If $z \times z = 36$, then $z =$ _____ | 100 ☐

END OF TEST

PAPER 3 TOTAL MARK ☐

Paper 4

MARK
✓ or ✗

Q. 1–5

multiplication problems

1 What is the product of five hundred and sixty-eight and seventeen? _____ 1 ☐

2 What is thirteen thousand and twelve multiplied by 30? _____ 2 ☐

3 If there are sixteen football teams in a league and thirteen players in each team, how many players are there altogether? _____ 3 ☐

4 Multiply 685 by the product of two and four. _____ 4 ☐

5 Multiply twenty-five by itself. _____ 5 ☐

Q. 6–10

division problems

6 Divide seven hundred and sixty-eight by eight. _____ 6 ☐

7 What is 3000 divided by 5? _____ 7 ☐

8 Divide 5 into a century. _____ 8 ☐

9 If 169 raspberries are shared among 13 people, how many does each person get? _____ 9 ☐

10 What is 27 642 divided by 6? _____ 10 ☐

Q. 11–15

scale

Amir draws a plan of his house and garden using a scale of 4cm to 9m.

11 How long is the hall if it measures 2cm on the plan? _____ m 11 ☐

12 How wide is his house if it measures 3cm on the plan? _____ m 12 ☐

13 His garden measures 22.5m long. How long will it be on the plan? _____ cm 13 ☐

14 The garden measures 13.5m wide. How wide will it be on the plan? _____ cm 14 ☐

15 His bedroom measures 1cm wide on the plan. What is its width in m? _____ m 15 ☐

Q. 16–20

fractions to percentages

Write down the shaded fraction of each box as a percentage.

16 _____ %
17 _____ %
18 _____ %
19 _____ %
20 _____ %

16 ☐
17 ☐
18 ☐
19 ☐
20 ☐

MARK ☐

MARK
✓ or ✗

Q. 21–25

measures addition and subtraction

21	l ml	22	kg g	23	£.p
	1 638		100 000		32.54
	2 046		− 36 527		− 17.28
	+7 009		————		————
	————				

24 Add together 3 days, 20 hours and 49 minutes to 2 days, 18 hours and 37 minutes. _____ d _____ h _____ min

25 3.6km – 0.75km = _____ km

21 ☐
22 ☐
23 ☐
24 ☐
25 ☐

Q. 26–30

prime numbers

15   79   4   48   37   22
7   64   17   98   9   53

Which of these numbers are prime numbers?

26 _____ 27 _____ 28 _____ 29 _____ 30 _____

26 ☐
27 ☐
28 ☐
29 ☐
30 ☐

Q. 31–35

24-hour clock

Change these a.m. and p.m. times to 24-hour clock times.

a.m.   noon   p.m.   p.m.   a.m.

31 _____ 32 _____ 33 _____ 34 _____ 35 _____

31 ☐
32 ☐
33 ☐
34 ☐
35 ☐

Q. 36–40

mass problems

36 Find the total of $6\frac{1}{4}$ kg, 7 kg 430 g and 5.4 kg. _____ kg _____ g

37 Add 7 kg to 6420 g and then subtract their difference. _____ kg _____ g

38 Three sacks of salt weigh 150 kg. What will a dozen sacks weigh? _____ kg

39 How many kg are there in 52 500 grams? _____ kg

40 A large bar of chocolate weighs 500 g. If it is shared among four children, how many grams should each child get? _____ g

36 ☐
37 ☐
38 ☐
39 ☐
40 ☐

MARK ☐

Maths
Progress Papers 1
Answers

Schofield & Sims

Maths Progress Papers 1

Notes for parents, tutors, teachers and other helpers

This pull-out book contains correct answers to all the questions in **Maths Progress Papers 1**, and is designed to assist you, the adult helper, as you mark the child's work. Once the child has become accustomed to the method of working, you may wish to give him or her direct access to this pull-out section.

When marking, put a tick or a cross in the tinted column on the far right of the question page. **Only one mark is available for each question**. Sub-total boxes at the foot of each page will help you to add marks quickly. You can then fill in the total marks at the end of the paper. The total score is out of 100 and can easily be turned into a percentage. The child's progress can be recorded using the **Progress chart** on page 48.

The child should aim to spend between 45 and 75 minutes on each paper, but may need more time, or more than one session, to complete the paper. The child should try to work on each paper when feeling fresh and free from distraction.

How to use the pull-out answers

This answer booklet contains answers to all the questions in the book to help with marking. Where the child has answered a question incorrectly, take time to look at the question and answer together and work out how the correct answer was achieved.

By working through the tests and corresponding answers, the child will start to recognise the clues that he or she should look for next time. These skills can then be put into practice by moving on to the next paper, as the difficultly increases incrementally throughout the series.

When a paper has been marked, notice if there are any topics that are proving particularly tricky. You may wish to complete some targeted practice in those areas, by focusing on that particular topic as it appears in each paper. For example, if a child has struggled with long multiplication, but answered all other questions accurately, you may wish to target only long multiplication questions in your next practice session. The **Topics chart**, available to download for free from the Schofield & Sims website, makes it easy to tailor practice to the child's individual needs.

Paper 1

1	59
2	962
3	9757
4	16
5	386
6	90p
7	100p
8	60p
9	40p
10	70p
11	108
12	200
13	1200
14	8613
15	6012
16	32
17	160
18	84
19	94
20	566
21	31
22	711
23	287
24	5050
25	three hundred and four
26	5152
27	1152
28	38 440
29	539
30	197 916
31	296
32	24
33	49
34	412
35	31
36	10.2
37	31.81
38	170.33
39	34.60
40	1.09
41	1 h 40 min
42	5 min
43	25 min
44	2 h 30 min
45	1 h 22 min

Paper 1 – *continued*

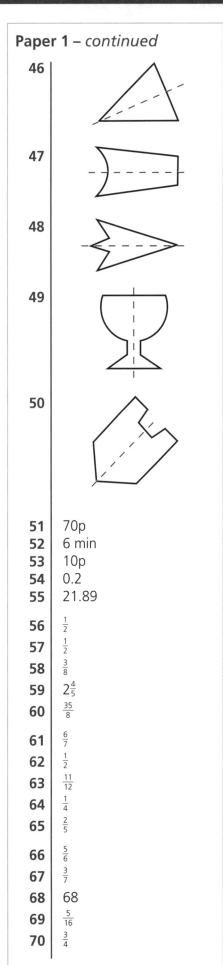

51	70p
52	6 min
53	10p
54	0.2
55	21.89
56	$\frac{1}{2}$
57	$\frac{1}{2}$
58	$\frac{3}{8}$
59	$2\frac{4}{5}$
60	$\frac{35}{8}$
61	$\frac{6}{7}$
62	$\frac{1}{2}$
63	$\frac{11}{12}$
64	$\frac{1}{4}$
65	$\frac{2}{5}$
66	$\frac{5}{6}$
67	$\frac{3}{7}$
68	68
69	$\frac{5}{16}$
70	$\frac{3}{4}$

Paper 1 – *continued*

71	50%
72	25%
73	75%
74	64
75	20%
76	18
77	15
78	3
79	19
80	16
81	£88.88
82	£66.60
83	£0.45
84	£23.15
85	£14.04

86–89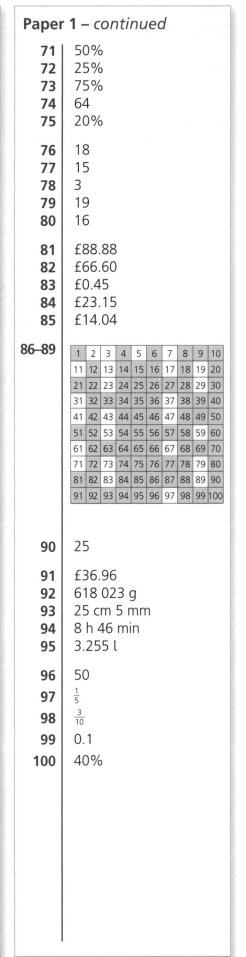

90	25
91	£36.96
92	618 023 g
93	25 cm 5 mm
94	8 h 46 min
95	3.255 l
96	50
97	$\frac{1}{5}$
98	$\frac{3}{10}$
99	0.1
100	40%

Paper 2

1	nine thousand four hundred and seven
2	seven thousand and five
3	thirty-six thousand four hundred and eighty-one
4	eighty-six thousand nine hundred and thirty-eight
5	eighty-six thousand nine hundred and sixty-four
6	860
7	3800
8	84 120
9	9334
10	3906
11	420
12	1742
13	4183
14	3220
15	7824
16	74.0
17	86.0
18	50.6
19	247.3
20	3.84
21	0.74
22	0.86
23	0.506
24	2.473
25	0.0384
26	65p
27	12 min
28	18 h
29	50p
30	49 km
31	$\frac{1}{12}$
32	$\frac{1}{6}$
33	$\frac{1}{18}$
34	$\frac{1}{9}$
35	$\frac{2}{7}$
36	A = 3, 9
37	B = 10, 7
38	C = 11, 4
39	D = 7, 2
40	E = 1, 6

Paper 2 – continued

41	$\frac{1}{3}$
42	14
43	$\frac{2}{5}$
44	600 ml
45	£17.50
46	25%
47	20%
48	50%
49	$12\frac{1}{2}$%
50	$33\frac{1}{3}$%
51	£97.92
52	35 315 g
53	518 562 ml
54	1 km 509 m
55	18 h
56	1, 2, 3, 4, 6, 12
57	1, 2, 3, 4, 6, 9, 12, 18, 36
58	1, 2, 3, 4, 6, 8, 12, 16, 24, 48
59	14, 28, 42, 56, 70
60	17, 34, 51, 68, 85
61	£67.50
62	£5.00
63	£143
64	£7.24
65	£200 000
66	trapezium
67	square
68	parallelogram
69	kite
70	rhombus
71	0900
72	1315
73	1800
74	2100
75	2300
76	25
77	54
78	58
79	19
80	2

Paper 2 – continued

81	24
82	56
83	4
84	35
85	6
86	<
87	>
88	<
89	=
90	>
91	
92	
93	
94	
95	

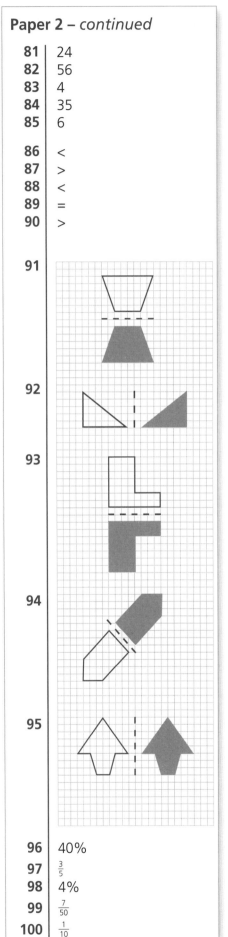

96	40%
97	$\frac{3}{5}$
98	4%
99	$\frac{7}{50}$
100	$\frac{1}{10}$

Paper 3

1
```
  2476
+1956
──────
  4432
```

2
```
  4896
+2058
──────
  6954
```

3
```
  3785
− 1454
──────
  2331
```

4
```
  275
×   6
──────
 1650
```

5
```
   184
 ─────
7)1288
```

6 8797
7 21 475
8 26 928
9 169 576
10 262 290

11 152.0
12 170.40
13 9.60
14 229.20
15 349.20

16 0.562
17 0.0562
18 0.2453
19 0.324
20 0.6

21 $\frac{12}{25}$
22 $\frac{7}{13}$
23 $\frac{3}{11}$
24 $\frac{2}{13}$
25 $\frac{9}{20}$

Paper 3 – *continued*

26 $5\frac{1}{4}$
27 $4\frac{1}{6}$
28 $9\frac{3}{4}$
29 $1\frac{5}{6}$
30 $1\frac{5}{12}$

31 $\frac{1}{2}$
32 $\frac{11}{20}$
33 $\frac{7}{40}$
34 $\frac{1}{5}$
35 $\frac{1}{10}$

36 135, 450, 90
37 60, 420, 120
38 528, 360, 796
39 $9 \times 5 \times 7$
40 $9 \times 3 \times 11$

41–45

46 19
47 39
48 306
49 38
50 47

51 48
52 7
53 16
54 25
55 18

56 $10\frac{1}{2}$
57 34
58 $1\frac{1}{3}$
59 9
60 5

61 £1.05
62 £1.54
63 £2.64
64 £1.08
65 £1.14

Paper 3 – *continued*

66 15 cm²
67 16 cm²
68 35 mm²
69 33 mm²
70 54 cm²

71 £1.60
72 £2.80
73 £4.00
74 £1.00
75 £3.80

76 ¥1800
77 £54
78 ¥9000
79 €84
80 £55

81 6
82 18
83 14
84 24
85 36

86 12 m
87 11
88 3 km 850 m
89 183 km
90 506 km 340 m

91 6000
92 40 000
93 50
94 6
95 12 000

96 5
97 13
98 6
99 31
100 6

Paper 4

1	9656
2	390 360
3	208
4	5480
5	625
6	96
7	600
8	20
9	13
10	4607
11	4.5 m
12	6.75 m
13	10 cm
14	6 cm
15	2.25 m
16	$37\frac{1}{2}\%$
17	$62\frac{1}{2}\%$
18	75%
19	60%
20	$87\frac{1}{2}\%$
21	10 693 ml
22	63 473 g
23	£15.26
24	6 d 15 h 26 min
25	2.85 km
26	7
27	17
28	37
29	53
30	79

(Answers may be in any order) — for 26–30

31	0345
32	1200
33	1725
34	2130
35	0020
36	19 kg 80 g
37	12 kg 840 g
38	600 kg
39	52.5 kg
40	125 g
41	£11.20
42	£1078
43	£4.80
44	£12.20
45	£18.56

Paper 4 – *continued*

46	acute
47	reflex
48	obtuse
49	right-angled
50	acute
51	140 442 m
52	£19.38
53	72 069 ml
54	17 wk 6 d
55	422 g
56	599 s
57	19 h 13 min
58	5 wk 0 d 2 h
59	95 min
60	$42\frac{1}{2}$ h

61
$$\begin{array}{r} 3758 \\ +2098 \\ \hline 5856 \end{array}$$

62
$$\begin{array}{r} 5798 \\ -3147 \\ \hline 2651 \end{array}$$

63
$$\begin{array}{r} 4271 \\ -3168 \\ \hline 1103 \end{array}$$

64
$$\begin{array}{r} 274 \\ \times 9 \\ \hline 2466 \end{array}$$

65
$$4\overline{)2344} = 586$$

66	$\frac{1}{2}$
67	$\frac{1}{6}$
68	$\frac{1}{6}$
69	$\frac{1}{3}$
70	$\frac{2}{3}$

Paper 4 – *continued*

71	21 cm
72	54 cm
73	72 cm
74	70 cm
75	48 cm
76	520
77	4800
78	4000
79	540 000
80	600 000
81	2 l 400 ml
82	55
83	13 l
84	15 l 750 ml
85	960 km
86	19
87	45
88	6
89	$\frac{5}{11}$
90	5
91	57
92	11
93	8
94	31
95	13
96	17, 21
97	23, 31
98	32, 64
99	4, 8
100	65, 61

Paper 5

1	146
2	1472
3	953
4	21 550
5	1818
6	B
7	20 min
8	2 h 56 min
9	1 h 23 min
10	17 h 25 min
11	115 070
12	98 008
13	120 502
14	500 006
15	227 080
16	80 000
17	300 000
18	4 206 587
19	55 000 000
20	500 000
21	52.18
22	147.54
23	189.09
24	174.91
25	281.75
26	A
27	H
28	B, C
29	X
30	O
31	20%
32	20%
33	$33\frac{1}{3}$%
34	$37\frac{1}{2}$%
35	20%
36	22
37	385
38	95
39	124
40	268
41	£10.75
42	£59.50
43	£8.40
44	£95.00
45	£25.60

Paper 5 – *continued*

46	122 m
47	100 000 cm
48	20
49	1 km 750 m
50	7 m 60 cm
51	$\frac{1}{5}$
52	$\frac{1}{4}$
53	$\frac{7}{12}$
54	$\frac{2}{5}$
55	$\frac{1}{10}$
56	£18.60
57	£208.80
58	£12.00
59	£26.30
60	20 wk
61	18
62	56
63	36
64	69
65	12
66	360°
67	1080°
68	720°
69	180°
70	540°
71	67
72	225
73	57
74	6.2
75	64
76	27, 38
77	21, 37
78	36, 21
79	25, 36
80	$1\frac{7}{8}$, 2
81	$5\frac{1}{2}$
82	$6\frac{1}{4}$
83	$\frac{1}{4}$
84	18
85	6

Paper 5 – *continued*

86	12
87	17
88	30
89	28
90	24
91	£20
92	£61
93	£3
94	£200
95	£50
96	216, 540, 720
97	450, 1260, 2430
98	30, 90, 120
99	$2 \times 4 \times 17$
100	$3 \times 5 \times 7$

Paper 6

1	1454
2	3573
3	19 682
4	3035
5	7356
6	10
7	11
8	3
9	7
10	5
11	581
12	3744
13	8988
14	2403
15	107 448
16	94
17	973
18	435
19	643
20	500
21	218 382
22	308 035
23	591 552
24	503 014
25	230 580
26	372
27	863
28	30
29	3
30	0.7
31	4.9
32	0.49
33	0.049
34	16.4
35	0.032
36	$4\frac{1}{6}$
37	$11\frac{3}{7}$
38	$13\frac{1}{12}$
39	$12\frac{3}{4}$
40	23

Paper 6 – continued

41	$\frac{19}{20}$
42	$\frac{1}{2}$
43	$1\frac{21}{40}$
44	$18\frac{7}{12}$
45	$14\frac{3}{16}$
46	80%
47	35%
48	16%
49	$66\frac{2}{3}$%
50	54%
51	parallel
52	perpendicular
53	parallel
54	perpendicular
55	perpendicular
56	250
57	60
58	2000
59	1000
60	30
61	6 a.m.
62	1°C
63	The heating is off.
64	4 p.m.
65	12°C

66
$$\begin{array}{r} 5289 \\ + 4269 \\ \hline 9558 \end{array}$$

67
$$\begin{array}{r} 7421 \\ - 3157 \\ \hline 4264 \end{array}$$

68
$$\begin{array}{r} 368 \\ \times 7 \\ \hline 2576 \end{array}$$

69
$$\begin{array}{r} 452 \\ \times 8 \\ \hline 3616 \end{array}$$

70
$$5\overline{)2890}\;\;578$$

Paper 6 – continued

71	36°
72	60°
73	30°
74	47°
75	133°
76	38 cm^2
77	38 cm^2
78	240 cm^2
79	402 mm^2
80	292 cm^2
81	210 km
82	624 sea miles
83	$31\frac{1}{2}$ km
84	315 km
85	2625 km
86	40 l 236 ml
87	58 l 375 ml
88	40 l
89	2 353 750 l
90	6386 l
91	97 d
92	523 s
93	1 000 000 cm^3
94	11 015 kg
95	1738p
96	£1059.68
97	£13.35
98	£10 725
99	£272.97
100	£215.06

Paper 7

1	1440 min
2	4164
3	744 h
4	512
5	68 inches
6	36 d
7	85
8	15
9	37
10	34
11	100
12	72
13	70
14	46
15	7
16	$\frac{3}{4}$
17	18
18	$\frac{1}{4}$
19	4
20	20

21–25

$\frac{7}{8}$	$1\frac{3}{4}$	$1\frac{1}{8}$
$1\frac{1}{2}$	$1\frac{1}{4}$	1
$1\frac{3}{8}$	$\frac{3}{4}$	$1\frac{5}{8}$

26

27

28

Paper 7 – continued

29

30

31	8, 9
32	9, 2
33	1, 10
34	1, 4
35	5, 6
36	10 kg 733 g
37	28 kg 560 g
38	20
39	150 kg
40	15 kg
41	yes
42	101, 103, 107, 109
43	6
44	no
45	17 53
46	10 000
47	40 763
48	12 000 020
49	3888
50	3361
51	90 km/h
52	15 km/h
53	960 km/h
54	100 km/h
55	12 km/h
56	4 km 800 m
57	9 km 180 m
58	92 cm 3 mm
59	1000 mm
60	737 m 40 cm

Paper 7 – continued

61	35 cm
62	30 cm
63	1.2 km
64	5 km
65	7.2 km
66	£196.10
67	£210
68	£2409
69	£399.50
70	£594
71	6 h
72	9 h
73	1230
74	24 min
75	1 h 50 min
76	5
77	7
78	4
79	3
80	5.2
81	£2.75 and £2.25
82	£8 and £2
83	3 m and $1\frac{1}{2}$ m
84	16 girls
85	90 cm and 10 cm
86	XVIII
87	LXXIX
88	LXXX
89	LVII
90	XCIX
91	84 cm²
92	76 cm²
93	80 m²
94	25 000 m²
95	24.48 m²
96	30°
97	120°
98	165°
99	330°
100	165°

This book of answers is a pull-out section from
Maths Progress Papers 1

Published by **Schofield & Sims Ltd**,
7 Mariner Court, Wakefield, West Yorkshire WF4 3FL, UK
Telephone 01484 607080
www.schofieldandsims.co.uk

First published in 1994
This edition copyright © Schofield & Sims, 2018
Fifth impression 2022

Author: **Patrick Berry**
Revised by Rebecca Brant and Peter Hall
Patrick Berry has asserted his moral rights under the Copyright, Designs
and Patents Act, 1988, to be identified as the author of this work.

British Library Cataloguing in Publication Data
A catalogue record for this book is available from the British Library.

Design by **Ledgard Jepson Ltd**

Printed in the UK by **Page Bros (Norwich) Ltd**

ISBN 978 07217 1456 1

MARK
✓ or ✗

Q. 41–45

money
problems

41 The fare from Bracknell to Camberley is £1.60 for an adult and half price for a child. How much would the return fare be for two adults and three children?   £ _____   41 ☐

42 From the sum of £768 and £539 take their difference.   £ _____   42 ☐

43 I spent half of my £30.60 savings on toys and another £10.50 on a DVD. How much had I left?   £ _____   43 ☐

44 I handed in to the school bank 70 pennies, 26 ten pences, 38 five pences, 6 fifty pence pieces and 4 pound coins. How much did I bank altogether?   £ _____   44 ☐

45 Alice bought four model cars costing £4.20, £3.72, £6.65 and £3.99. How much did she spend in total?   £ _____   45 ☐

Q. 46–50

angles and
degrees

Use the terms acute, obtuse, reflex and right-angled to describe the following angles:

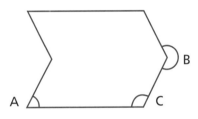

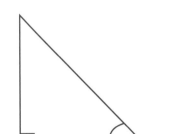

46 A _____   46 ☐

47 B _____   47 ☐

48 C _____   48 ☐

49 D _____   49 ☐

50 E _____   50 ☐

Q. 51–55

measures
multiplication
and division

51

km m
23 407
× 6
_____
_____

52

4)£77.52

53

12)864 828ml

54 3 weeks and 4 days × 5 =   _____ wk _____ d

55 Divide 3kg 798g by 9.   _____ g

51 ☐
52 ☐
53 ☐
54 ☐
55 ☐

MARK ☐

MARK
✓ or ✗

Q. 56–60

time problems

56 Change 9 min 59 s to seconds. _____ s | 56

57 Change 1153 min to hours and minutes. _____ h _____ min | 57

58 Change 842 hours to weeks, days and hours. _____ wk _____ d _____ h | 58

59 How many minutes are there between 1132 hours and 1307 hours? _____ min | 59

60 A woman starts work at 0800 and works until 1730. If she has one hour for lunch, how many hours does she work in a five-day week? _____ h | 60

Q. 61–65

missing numbers

61
```
  □ 7 5 8
+ 2 0 □ □
─────────
  5 □ 5 6
```
| 61

62
```
  5 7 □ 8
- □ 1 4 □
─────────
  2 □ 5 1
```
| 62

63
```
  □ 2 7 1
- 3 □ 6 □
─────────
  1 1 □ 3
```
| 63

64
```
    2 □ 4
  ×     9
─────────
  □ 4 6 □
```

65
```
      5 □ 6
    _____
4 ) □ 3 4 4
```
| 64
| 65

Q. 66–70

probability

If Jamal throws a die, he may throw 1 or 2 or 3 or 4 or 5 or 6. His chances of throwing an even number are 2 in 6, or $\frac{3}{6}$, or $\frac{1}{2}$.

Answer each question below, giving a fraction in its lowest form.

66 What are Jamal's chances of throwing an odd number? _____ | 66

67 What are his chances of throwing a six? _____ | 67

68 What are his chances of throwing a four? _____ | 68

69 What are his chances of throwing a number less than three? _____ | 69

70 What are his chances of throwing a number greater than two? _____ | 70

MARK [_____]

Schofield & Sims • Maths Progress Papers 1

MARK
✓ or ✗

Q. 71–75

perimeters

What are the perimeters of these regular shapes?

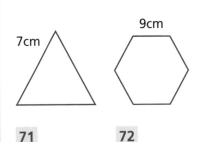

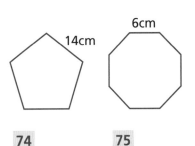

7cm

9cm

18cm

14cm

6cm

71 _____ cm

72 _____ cm

73 _____ cm

74 _____ cm

75 _____ cm

71 ☐
72 ☐
73 ☐
74 ☐
75 ☐

Q. 76–80

estimation
and
approximation

76 Round 519 to the nearest 10. _____

77 Round 4763 to the nearest 100. _____

78 Round 3850 to the nearest 1000. _____

79 Round 543 216 to the nearest 10 000. _____

80 Round 618 209 to the nearest 100 000. _____

76 ☐
77 ☐
78 ☐
79 ☐
80 ☐

Q. 81–85

capacity
problems

81 Water leaks from a tap at a rate of
200 ml every 5 minutes. How much
will leak in one hour? _____ l _____ ml

82 A tank holds 330 litres. How many times
can a 6-litre bucket be filled from it? _____

83 On a hot day a shop sold 87 000 ml of orange
juice out of a total stock of 100 litres. How many
litres were left at the end of the day? _____ l

84 A family drinks, on average, $2\frac{1}{4}$ litres
of milk each day. How much do they
drink in a week? _____ l _____ ml

85 If a car travels 12 km on each litre of
petrol, how far will it go on 80 litres? _____ km

81 ☐
82 ☐
83 ☐
84 ☐
85 ☐

Q. 86–90

mean,
median,
mode and
range

Find the mean of the numbers inside each circle.

20 19 18

45 55 35

1 7 9 5 11 3

$\frac{7}{11}$ 3 $\frac{3}{11}$

8 9 0 4 3 6

86 _____

87 _____

88 _____

89 _____

90 _____

86 ☐
87 ☐
88 ☐
89 ☐
90 ☐

MARK ☐

MARK
✓ or ✗

Q. 91–95

BODMAS

| 91 | $4 (3 \times 4) + 3^2 =$ | _____ | 91 ☐ |

| 92 | $5 + 3 \times 8 \div 4 =$ | _____ | 92 ☐ |

| 93 | $10 - 2 \times 4 + 6 =$ | _____ | 93 ☐ |

| 94 | $3 + 2 (2 \times 7) =$ | _____ | 94 ☐ |

| 95 | $16 - 2 \times 4 + 15 \div 3 =$ | _____ | 95 ☐ |

Q. 96–100

sequences

Write the next two terms in each of these sequences.

96	1	5	9	13	_____ _____	96 ☐
97	1	5	10	16	_____ _____	97 ☐
98	2	4	8	16	_____ _____	98 ☐
99	$\frac{1}{4}$	$\frac{1}{2}$	1	2	_____ _____	99 ☐
100	81	77	73	69	_____ _____	100 ☐

END OF TEST

PAPER 4 TOTAL MARK ☐

START HERE

MARK
✓ or ✗

Q. 1–5

addition and subtraction problems

1 Add together eighty-nine and fifty-seven. _____ 1 ☐

2 How many is eight hundred and ninety-three plus seventy, plus five hundred and nine? _____ 2 ☐

3 Increase five hundred and fifty-seven by three hundred and ninety-six. _____ 3 ☐

4 A builder estimated that one wall would need 4050 bricks, a second wall would need eight thousand and a third would need 9500. How many bricks would be needed altogether? _____ 4 ☐

5 What is the new total if the sum of 876 and 590 is increased by 352? _____ 5 ☐

Q. 6–10

timetables

Bus timetable: Falkirk – Dunipace – Falkirk

	Falkirk	Bonnybridge	Denny	Dunipace	Denny	Bonnybridge	Falkirk
A	0745	0759	0806	0819	0832	0839	0853
B	0909	0922	0929	0942	0955	1002	1016
C	1312	1326	1333	1346	1359	1406	1420

6 Which bus, A, B or C, takes the shortest time to complete the entire journey? _____ 6 ☐

7 If I board bus A at Bonnybridge, how long will it take me to get to Dunipace? _____ min 7 ☐

8 If I get off bus B in Falkirk to do some shopping, how long will I have before catching the next bus home? _____ h _____ min 8 ☐

9 If I leave bus A in Dunipace, how long must I wait for the next bus? _____ h _____ min 9 ☐

10 How much time is there between the last bus arriving back at Falkirk and the first bus next day leaving Falkirk? _____ h _____ min 10 ☐

Q. 11–15

writing large numbers

Write each of these numbers in figures.

11 one hundred and fifteen thousand and seventy _____ 11 ☐

12 ninety-eight thousand and eight _____ 12 ☐

13 one hundred and twenty thousand five hundred and two _____ 13 ☐

14 five hundred thousand and six _____ 14 ☐

15 two hundred and twenty-seven thousand and eighty _____ 15 ☐

MARK ☐

MARK
✓ or ✗

Q. 16–20

large number problems

16 Write down the value of the eight in the number 384 000. _____ | 16 ☐

17 What is the value of the three in the number 7 349 622? _____ | 17 ☐

18 Multiply six hundred thousand nine hundred and forty-one by seven. _____ | 18 ☐

19 Write the population of England and Wales (55 240 475) to the nearest million. _____ | 19 ☐

20 Divide three million by six. _____ | 20 ☐

Q. 21–25

decimal addition and subtraction

21	22	23	24	25
17.26 25.84 + 9.08	36.79 15.88 + 94.87	100.04 3.76 + 85.29	462.35 − 287.44	681.17 − 399.42

21 ☐
22 ☐
23 ☐
24 ☐
25 ☐

Q. 26–30

symmetry

26 Which letter has just one line of symmetry (vertical)? _____ | 26 ☐

27 Which letter has just two lines of symmetry? _____ | 27 ☐

28 Which letters have only one horizontal line of symmetry? _____ | 28 ☐

29 Which letter has only four lines of symmetry? _____ | 29 ☐

30 Which letter has many lines of symmetry? _____ | 30 ☐

Q. 31–35

percentage problems

31 What percentage of twelve and a half litres is two and a half litres? _____% | 31 ☐

32 What percentage of 1 hr 20 min is 16 min? _____% | 32 ☐

33 What percentage of $\frac{3}{4}$ is $\frac{1}{4}$? _____% | 33 ☐

34 What percentage of 48p is 18p? _____% | 34 ☐

35 What percentage of 200 is 40? _____% | 35 ☐

MARK ☐

MARK
✓ or ✗

Q. 36–40

long division

36	37	38	39	40

$21\overline{)462}$ $18\overline{)6930}$ $34\overline{)3230}$ $25\overline{)3100}$ $37\overline{)9916}$

36	
37	
38	
39	
40	

Q. 41–45

using money

Work out the total for each line of this bill, so that they all add up to the total given.

Birch Wood DIY Supplies

£ . p

41   5 litres of paint at £2.15 per litre   =

42   7 bags of charcoal at £8.50 each   =

43   12 bags of nails at 70p each   =

44   4 hammers at £23.75 each   =

45   80 metres of wallpaper at 32p per metre   =

            Total =   199.25

41	
42	
43	
44	
45	

Q. 46–50

length problems

46   A bus is 11.3 m long. If ten buses are parked one behind the other with a metre between them, how long is the line of buses? Use the diagram above to help you.   _____ m

47   How many centimetres are there in a kilometre?   _____ cm

48   A swimming pool is 50 metres wide. How many times must I cross it in order to swim one kilometre?   _____

49   Take $\frac{1}{3}$ of 6 km from $\frac{1}{2}$ of 7500 m.   _____ km _____ m

50   From the sum of $3\frac{4}{5}$ metres and $7\frac{1}{4}$ metres take their difference.   _____ m _____ cm

46	
47	
48	
49	
50	

MARK

MARK
✓ or ✗

Q. 51–55

bar charts

This is a bar chart showing the hobbies of a group of people.
Each person named his or her favourite hobby.

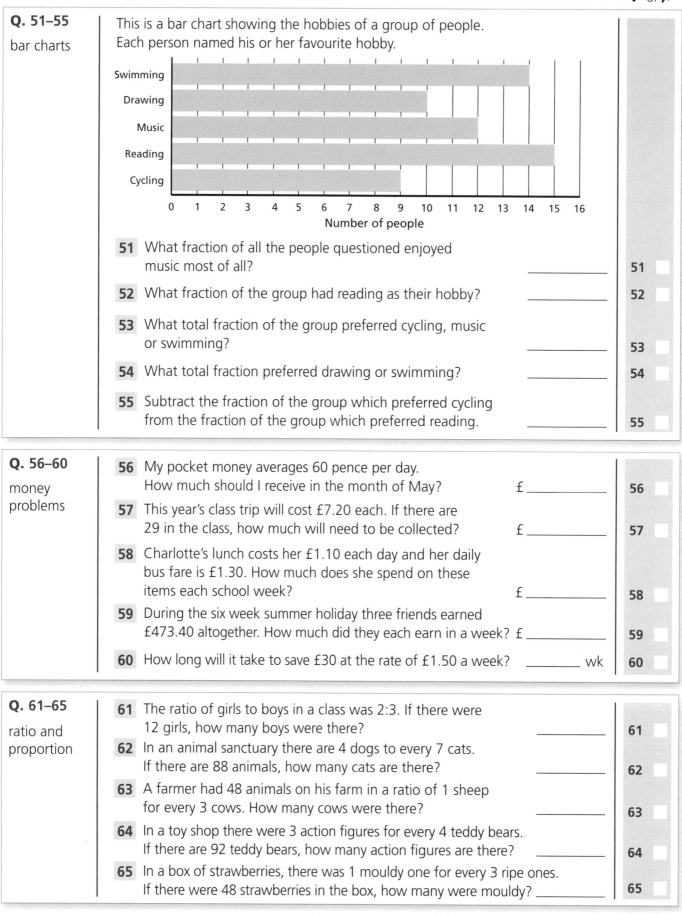

Number of people

51 What fraction of all the people questioned enjoyed
music most of all? _____ 51 ☐

52 What fraction of the group had reading as their hobby? _____ 52 ☐

53 What total fraction of the group preferred cycling, music
or swimming? _____ 53 ☐

54 What total fraction preferred drawing or swimming? _____ 54 ☐

55 Subtract the fraction of the group which preferred cycling
from the fraction of the group which preferred reading. _____ 55 ☐

Q. 56–60

money
problems

56 My pocket money averages 60 pence per day.
How much should I receive in the month of May? £ _____ 56 ☐

57 This year's class trip will cost £7.20 each. If there are
29 in the class, how much will need to be collected? £ _____ 57 ☐

58 Charlotte's lunch costs her £1.10 each day and her daily
bus fare is £1.30. How much does she spend on these
items each school week? £ _____ 58 ☐

59 During the six week summer holiday three friends earned
£473.40 altogether. How much did they each earn in a week? £ _____ 59 ☐

60 How long will it take to save £30 at the rate of £1.50 a week? _____ wk 60 ☐

Q. 61–65

ratio and
proportion

61 The ratio of girls to boys in a class was 2:3. If there were
12 girls, how many boys were there? _____ 61 ☐

62 In an animal sanctuary there are 4 dogs to every 7 cats.
If there are 88 animals, how many cats are there? _____ 62 ☐

63 A farmer had 48 animals on his farm in a ratio of 1 sheep
for every 3 cows. How many cows were there? _____ 63 ☐

64 In a toy shop there were 3 action figures for every 4 teddy bears.
If there are 92 teddy bears, how many action figures are there? _____ 64 ☐

65 In a box of strawberries, there was 1 mouldy one for every 3 ripe ones.
If there were 48 strawberries in the box, how many were mouldy? _____ 65 ☐

MARK ☐

MARK
✓ or ✗

Q. 66–70

angles and degrees

How many degrees does each of these regular shapes have?

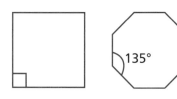   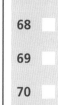

66   67   68   69   70

_____ _____ _____ _____ _____

66 ☐
67 ☐
68 ☐
69 ☐
70 ☐

Q. 71–75

what is my number?

71 I think of a prime number. The sum of its digits is 13. What is my number? _____

72 My number is the product of two square numbers. The sum of the two square numbers is 34. What is my number? _____

73 My number is the middle of 3 consecutive numbers. The sum of the 3 numbers is 171. What is my number? _____

74 I think of a number halfway between 4.9 and 7.5. What is my number? _____

75 I think of a square number whose two digits add to 10. What is my number? _____

71 ☐
72 ☐
73 ☐
74 ☐
75 ☐

Q. 76–80

sequences

Write the next two terms in each of these sequences.

76   3   6   11   18   _____ _____

77   6   7   9   13   _____ _____

78   66   63   57   48   _____ _____

79   1   4   9   16   _____ _____

80 $1\frac{3}{8}$ $1\frac{1}{2}$ $1\frac{5}{8}$ $1\frac{3}{4}$ _____ _____

76 ☐
77 ☐
78 ☐
79 ☐
80 ☐

Q. 81–85

algebra

81 If $s - 2 = 3\frac{1}{2}$, then $s =$ _____

82 If $n + 5 = 11\frac{1}{4}$, then $n =$ _____

83 If $\frac{1}{2}z = \frac{1}{8}$, then $z =$ _____

84 If $\frac{6}{p} = \frac{1}{3}$, then $p =$ _____

85 If $\frac{9}{t} = 1\frac{1}{2}$, then $t =$ _____

81 ☐
82 ☐
83 ☐
84 ☐
85 ☐

MARK ☐

MARK
✓ or ✗

Q. 86–90

factors and
multiples

86 What is the highest common factor of 24 and 36? _____ 86 ☐

87 What is the highest common factor of 51 and 68? _____ 87 ☐

88 What is the lowest common multiple of 6 and 10? _____ 88 ☐

89 What is the lowest common multiple of 4 and 7? _____ 89 ☐

90 What is the lowest common multiple of 8 and 12? _____ 90 ☐

Q. 91–95

currency
conversion

Use the currency conversion table below to answer the questions below.

Pound sterling	Australian dollar	Kenyan shilling	Norwegian krone	Swiss franc
£1	$1.7	KSh130	kr9	CHF1.4

How much would the following items cost in British pounds?

91 A pair of trousers costing $34. £ _____ 91 ☐

92 A table costing kr549. £ _____ 92 ☐

93 A box of doughnuts costing CHF4.2. £ _____ 93 ☐

94 A television costing KSh26000. £ _____ 94 ☐

95 An electric drill costing $85. £ _____ 95 ☐

Q. 96–100

divisibility
rules

96 Circle the numbers which are divisible by both 9 and 4.
451 216 540 720 688
96 ☐

97 Circle the numbers which are divisible by both 10 and 9.
450 1260 279 640 2430
97 ☐

98 Circle the numbers which are divisible by 2, 3 and 5.
30 15 90 120 40
98 ☐

Use your knowledge of divisibility rules to complete the following sums.

99 ___ × ___ × ___ = 136
99 ☐

100 ___ × ___ × ___ = 105
100 ☐

END OF TEST

PAPER 5 TOTAL MARK ☐

Paper 6

MARK
✓ or ✗

Q. 1–5

simple addition and subtraction

1

```
  4307
- 2853
_____
```

2

```
  7001
- 3428
_____
```

3

```
  7493
  6287
+ 5902
_____
```

4

```
   797
   894
   263
   875
+  206
_____
```

5 6074 + 38 + 908 + 4 + 332 = _____

1	☐
2	☐
3	☐
4	☐
5	☐

Q. 6–10

pie charts

This pie chart shows how 36 children travel to school each day.
Use your protractor to help you work out the answers.

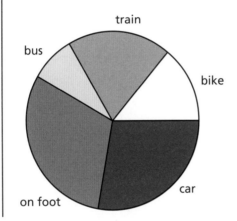

How many children travel to school:

6 by car? _____

7 on foot? _____

8 by bus? _____

9 by train? _____

10 by bike? _____

6	☐
7	☐
8	☐
9	☐
10	☐

Q. 11–15

simple multiplication

11

```
  83
×  7
____
```

12

```
 468
×  8
____
```

13

```
 749
× 12
____
```

14

```
 267
×  9
____
```

15

```
9768
×  11
____
```

11	☐
12	☐
13	☐
14	☐
15	☐

Q. 16–20

simple division

16 8)752

17 9)8757

18 11)4785

19 7)4501

20 8)4000

16	☐
17	☐
18	☐
19	☐
20	☐

MARK ☐

MARK
✓ or ✗

Q. 21–25

long multiplication

21	22	23	24
6423 ×34	4739 ×65	7584 ×78	5849 ×86

25 What is 2745 multiplied by 84?

21	
22	
23	
24	
25	

Q. 26–30

decimal multiplication

26 3.72 × 100 =

27 8.63 × 100 =

28 0.3 × 100 =

29 0.03 × 100 =

30 0.007 × 100 =

26	
27	
28	
29	
30	

Q. 31–35

decimal division

31 49 ÷ 10 =

32 49 ÷ 100 =

33 49 ÷ 1000 =

34 98.4 ÷ 6 =

35 0.224 ÷ 7 =

31	
32	
33	
34	
35	

Q. 36–40

reduce to lowest terms

Write these improper fractions as mixed numbers in their lowest terms.

36	37	38	39	40
$\frac{25}{6} =$	$\frac{80}{7} =$	$\frac{157}{12} =$	$\frac{102}{8} =$	$\frac{138}{6} =$

36	
37	
38	
39	
40	

Q. 41–45

fraction addition and subtraction

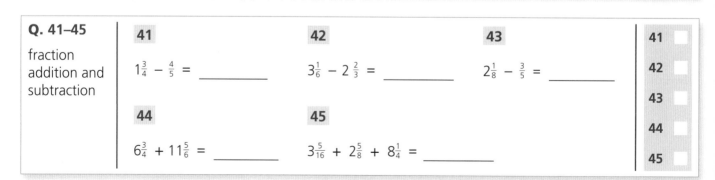

41

$1\frac{3}{4} - \frac{4}{5} =$ _____

42

$3\frac{1}{6} - 2\frac{2}{3} =$ _____

43

$2\frac{1}{8} - \frac{3}{5} =$ _____

44

$6\frac{3}{4} + 11\frac{5}{6} =$ _____

45

$3\frac{5}{16} + 2\frac{5}{8} + 8\frac{1}{4} =$ _____

41	
42	
43	
44	
45	

MARK [ ]

MARK
✓ or ✗

Q. 46–50

fractions to
percentages

What percentage of each of these shapes is shaded?

46

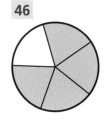

_____ %

47

_____ %

48

_____ %

49

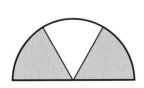

_____ %

50

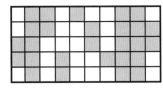

_____ %

46	☐
47	☐
48	☐
49	☐
50	☐

Q. 51–55

shape
properties

Look at the two shapes below:

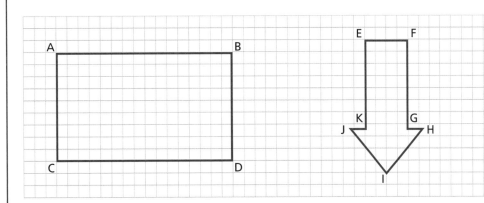

Describe the following lines using the words **parallel** or **perpendicular.**

51 AB is _____ to CD

52 CD is _____ to BD

53 EF is _____ to JK

54 FG is _____ to GH

55 IJ is _____ to HI

51	☐
52	☐
53	☐
54	☐
55	☐

MARK ☐

MARK
✓ or ✗

Q. 56–60

estimation and approximation

Estimate the answers to these questions by approximating.
Underline the answer. Do not try to work out the exact answer.

| 56 | 25 × 9 = | 190 | 250 | 300 | 275 | 260 |

56 ☐

| 57 | 486 ÷ 8 = | 45 | 50 | 58 | 65 | 60 |

57 ☐

| 58 | 104 × 19 = | 2000 | 1850 | 2200 | 1800 | 2500 |

58 ☐

| 59 | 252 × 4 = | 780 | 1100 | 900 | 850 | 1000 |

59 ☐

| 60 | 298 ÷ 9 = | 30 | 28 | 35 | 25 | 40 |

60 ☐

Q. 61–65

graphs

This graph shows the temperature of a classroom during a twenty-four hour period in January.

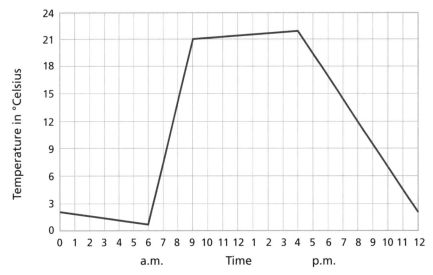

61 At what time is the heating switched on? _____ 61 ☐

62 What is the room temperature when this happens? _____ 62 ☐

63 Why do you think the temperature is so low from midnight until early morning?

_____ 63 ☐

64 At what time is the heating switched off? _____ 64 ☐

65 What is the temperature at 8 p.m.? _____ 65 ☐

MARK ☐

MARK
✓ or ✗

Q. 66–70

missing
numbers

66 ☐ 2 ☐ 9
　+　4　2　6　☐
　――――――――
　　9　☐　5　8

67　7　4　2　☐
　−　☐　1　☐　7
　――――――――
　　4　☐　6　4

68　☐　6　☐
　×　　　　　7
　――――――――
　2　☐　7　6

69　☐　5　2
　×　　　　8
　――――――――
　3　6　☐　6

70
　　　☐　7　8
　5)2　8　9　☐

66	☐
67	☐
68	☐
69	☐
70	☐

Q. 71–75

angles and
degrees

Calculate the following angles.

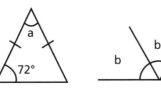

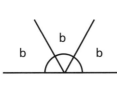

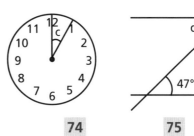

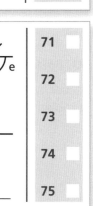

71　　　**72**　　　**73**　　　**74**　　　**75**

a _____　b _____　c _____　d _____　e _____

71	☐
72	☐
73	☐
74	☐
75	☐

Q. 76–80

area of
shapes

From the dimensions given, give the area of each compound shape.

4cm
8cm
2cm
7cm

5cm
2cm
9cm
4cm

13cm
15cm
9cm
5cm

76
_____ cm²

77
_____ cm²

78
_____ cm²

31mm
8mm
22mm
7mm

18cm
9cm
14cm
26cm

79
_____ mm²

80
_____ cm²

76	☐
77	☐
78	☐
79	☐
80	☐

MARK ☐

MARK
✓ or ✗

Q. 81–85	81	A car travels at 60 km/h. How far will it go between 9.00 a.m. and 12.30 p.m.? _____ km	81 ☐
distance = speed × time	82	If a submarine's speed is a constant 26 sea miles per hour, how far will it travel in 24 hours? _____ sea miles	82 ☐
	83	If I hike for 7 hours at a mean speed of $4\frac{1}{2}$ km/h, how far will I walk altogether? _____ km	83 ☐
	84	A train travelled at 140 km/h. How far did it travel in 2 h 15 min? _____ km	84 ☐
	85	How far away was my holiday destination if my aeroplane flew for $3\frac{1}{2}$ hours at 750 km/h? _____ km	85 ☐

Q. 86–90	86	Add $12\frac{3}{4}$ litres and 7 l 14 ml and subtract the total from 60 litres. _____ l _____ ml	86 ☐
capacity problems	87	Multiply $7\frac{5}{8}$ litres by 5 and add $20\frac{1}{4}$ litres to the total. _____ l _____ ml	87 ☐
	88	A litre of cooking oil costs £1.46. How many litres will £58.40 buy? _____ l	88 ☐
	89	Five tanks each have a capacity of 470 750 litres. What is the total capacity of them all? _____ l	89 ☐
	90	A shop sells 206 litres of milk each day. How much is sold in the month of August? _____ l	90 ☐

Q. 91–95	91	Convert 13 weeks 6 days to days. _____ d	91 ☐
measures conversion	92	Convert 8 min 43 s to seconds. _____ s	92 ☐
	93	Convert 1 cubic metre to cm³. _____ cm³	93 ☐
	94	Convert 11 tonnes 15 kg to kg. _____ kg	94 ☐
	95	Convert £17.38 to pence. _____ p	95 ☐

Q. 96–100	96	To one thousand and forty pounds add nineteen pounds and sixty-eight pence. £ _____	96 ☐
money problems	97	Imogen bought fruit costing £2.70, meat costing £8.95 and her bus fare to the shops was 85 pence each way. How much did she spend in total? £ _____	97 ☐
	98	A dealer bought a car for £8765. If he expected to make £1960 profit, at what price did he offer to sell it? £ _____	98 ☐
	99	Find three times the difference between £10.01 and £101.00. £ _____	99 ☐
	100	Mum's bank account had £375.06 in it before she withdrew £70 and £90. How much was left in the account then? £ _____	100 ☐

END OF TEST

PAPER 6 TOTAL MARK ☐

Paper 7

MARK
✓ or ✗

Q. 1–5

multiplication problems

1 How many minutes are there in one day? _____ min | 1 ☐

2 What is the product of 347 and 12? _____ | 2 ☐

3 How many hours are there in May? _____ h | 3 ☐

4 How many people altogether can be carried by eight 64-seater coaches? _____ | 4 ☐

5 The height of a horse is measured in hands. If a hand is four inches, how high to the shoulder (in inches) is a horse of seventeen hands? _____ inches | 5 ☐

Q. 6–10

division problems

6 How many days will four and a half tonnes of potatoes last if 125 kg are used each day? _____ d | 6 ☐

7 How many 15 cm wide tiles will be needed in each row of a wall which is 12.75 metres long? _____ | 7 ☐

8 How many 36p pears can be bought for £5.40? _____ | 8 ☐

9 In his cricket test career a bowler took 76 wickets for 2812 runs. How many runs is this per wicket? _____ | 9 ☐

10 How many sandwiches costing £1.50 each can be bought for £51? _____ | 10 ☐

Q. 11–15

BODMAS

11 $5^2 (2 \times 2) =$ _____ | 11 ☐

12 $15 + 9 \times 7 - 6 =$ _____ | 12 ☐

13 $42 + (8 \times 7) \div 2 =$ _____ | 13 ☐

14 $14 \times 3 + 7 - 9 \div 3 =$ _____ | 14 ☐

15 $(4 \times 7) \div (36 \div 9) =$ _____ | 15 ☐

Q. 16–20

fraction multiplication and division

16 $1\frac{1}{2} \times \frac{1}{2} =$ _____ | 16 ☐

17 $4\frac{1}{2} \div \frac{1}{4} =$ _____ | 17 ☐

18 $\frac{1}{3}$ of $\frac{3}{4} =$ _____ | 18 ☐

19 $2\frac{2}{3} \div \frac{2}{3} =$ _____ | 19 ☐

20 $3\frac{1}{3} \div \frac{1}{6} =$ _____ | 20 ☐

MARK ☐

MARK
✓ or ✗

Q. 21–25

magic
squares:
fractions

$\frac{7}{8}$		$1\frac{1}{8}$
	$1\frac{1}{4}$	
$1\frac{3}{8}$		

Fill in the missing figures in this magic
square so that all lines, diagonal, horizontal
and vertical, add up to the same total.

21 ☐

22 ☐

23 ☐

24 ☐

25 ☐

Q. 26–30

reflection and
rotation

Rotate the shapes 90° clockwise around the given point.

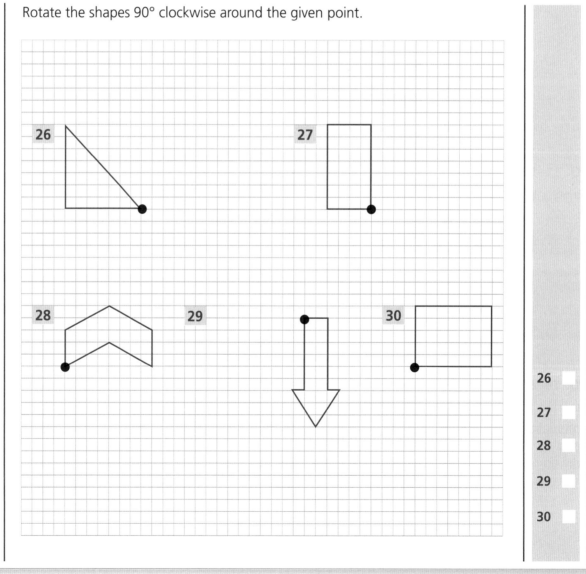

26 ☐

27 ☐

28 ☐

29 ☐

30 ☐

MARK ☐

MARK
✓ or ✗

Q. 31–35

coordinates

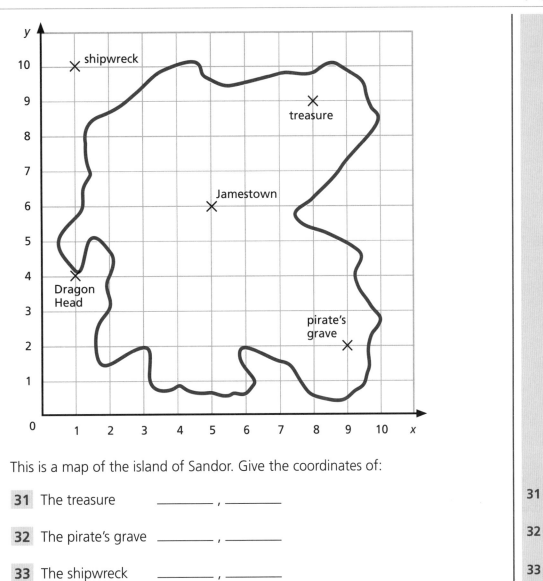

This is a map of the island of Sandor. Give the coordinates of:

31 The treasure _____ , _____

32 The pirate's grave _____ , _____

33 The shipwreck _____ , _____

34 Dragon Head _____ , _____

35 Jamestown _____ , _____

31 ☐

32 ☐

33 ☐

34 ☐

35 ☐

Q. 36–40

mass problems

36 Add together 7 kg, $2\frac{1}{4}$ kg and 1.483 kg. _____ kg _____ g

37 Multiply 4 kg 80 g by 7. _____ kg _____ g

38 A truck carries 1500 kg. How many truck loads will it take to move 30 000 kg? _____

39 Twenty sacks of corn weigh 3000 kg. What is the mass of one sack? _____ kg

40 A laptop weighs $1\frac{1}{4}$ kg. What will a dozen weigh? _____ kg

36 ☐

37 ☐

38 ☐

39 ☐

40 ☐

MARK ☐

MARK
✓ or ✗

Q. 41–45

prime numbers

41 Can the product of two whole numbers be a prime number? _____ | 41 ☐

42 Write down all the prime numbers between 100 and 110.

_____ | 42 ☐

43 How many prime numbers are there between 10 and 30? _____ | 43 ☐

44 Can any number (apart from 1) be a prime number when doubled? _____ | 44 ☐

45 Underline the prime numbers in this list: 17   46   9   99   53 | 45 ☐

Q. 46–50

large number problems

46 What does 100 become when multiplied by itself? _____ | 46 ☐

47 Add 700 to forty thousand and sixty-three. _____ | 47 ☐

48 Multiply three million and five by twelve and divide the answer by three. _____ | 48 ☐

49 Of four thousand and fifty eggs, one hundred and sixty-two were broken. How many eggs were whole? _____ | 49 ☐

50 Tutankhamun became king in 1347 BCE How many years were there between then and CE 2014? _____ | 50 ☐

Q. 51–55

speed = distance ÷ time

51 How many kilometres per hour must I drive to travel 450 km in 5 hours? _____ km/h | 51 ☐

52 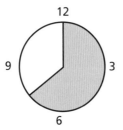 In a race a man covers 10 km in 40 minutes. What is his speed in km/h?

_____ km/h | 52 ☐

53 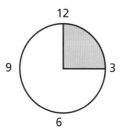 What is the speed of an aeroplane which covers 240 km in 15 minutes?

_____ km/h | 53 ☐

54 At what speed is a train travelling if it covers 325 km between 1000 h and 1315 h? _____ km/h | 54 ☐

55 Lily cycles 63 km in 5 h 15 min. What is her speed? _____ km/h | 55 ☐

MARK ☐

MARK
✓ or ✗

Q. 56–60

length problems

56 A garden is 60 m long and 20 m wide. If I walk round it 30 times, what distance do I cover? _____ km _____ m | **56**

57 Add together $\frac{7}{8}$ km, 6930 m and $1\frac{3}{8}$ km. _____ km _____ m | **57**

58 What must be added to 77 mm to make a metre? _____ cm _____ mm | **58**

59 How many millimetres are there in a metre? _____ mm | **59**

60 To the sum of $97\frac{4}{5}$ m and $368\frac{7}{10}$ m add their difference. _____ m _____ cm | **60**

Q. 61–65

scale

61 A road is 35 km long. How long will it be on a map with a scale of 1:100,000? _____ cm | **61**

62 A railway is 150 km long. How long will it be on a map with a scale of 1:500,000? _____ cm | **62**

63 A field measures 3 cm long on a map. If the scale of the map is 1:40,000 what is the length of the field in km? _____ km | **63**

64 On a map with a scale of 1:50,000 a river is 10 cm long. How long is it in km? _____ km | **64**

65 The distance in a straight line between two cities measures 9 cm on a map. If the scale of the map is 1:80,000 what is the distance between the two cities in km? _____ km | **65**

Q. 66–70

money problems

66 Oliver is paid £5.30 per hour. How much does he earn for a working week of thirty-seven hours? £ _____ | **66**

67 Find the cost of a tonne of coal at £10.50 per 50-kg sack. £ _____ | **67**

68 The school library needs to buy 11 new sets of shelves. If one set costs £219, how much will 11 cost? £ _____ | **68**

69 If it costs £23.50 to dump a lorry-load of waste, how much will it cost to dump seventeen lorry-loads? £ _____ | **69**

70 Our mean monthly gas bill is £49.50. How much do we pay in a year? £ _____ | **70**

Q. 71–75

time = distance ÷ speed

71 How long will a walker take to travel 21 km if she walks at an average speed of $3\frac{1}{2}$ km/h? _____ h | **71**

72 If I drive at 80 km/h for 720 kilometres, how long will I be driving? _____ h | **72**

73 A plane left Manchester at 0800 and flew for 3600 km at 800 km/h. At what time did it land? _____ | **73**

74 A train travels 1 kilometre every 15 seconds. How long will a journey of 96 kilometres take? _____ min | **74**

75 A car travels 165 km at a speed of $1\frac{1}{2}$ kilometres per minute. How many hours and minutes will the journey take? _____ h _____ min | **75**

MARK [ ]

MARK
✓ or ✗

Q. 76–80

mean,
median,
mode and
range

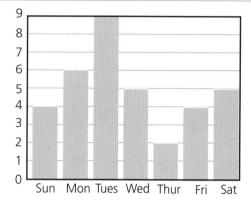

This histogram shows the number of orders for mushroom pizza at a local takeaway in one week.

76 What was the mean number of orders per day throughout the week? _____ | 76 ☐

77 What was the mean number of orders for Tuesday and Wednesday? _____ | 77 ☐

78 How many more than the daily mean was the number of orders on Tuesday? _____ | 78 ☐

79 How many less than the daily mean was the number of orders on Thursday? _____ | 79 ☐

80 Using a decimal, write down the mean number of orders per day from Monday to Friday. _____ | 80 ☐

Q. 81–85

unequal
sharing

81 Divide £5 between 2 children so that one gets 50p more than the other. £_____ and £_____ | 81 ☐

82 Divide £10 between 2 children so that one gets 4 times as much as the other. £_____ and £_____ | 82 ☐

83 A plank $4\frac{1}{2}$ metres long is cut into 2 parts so that one part is twice as long as the other. How long are the 2 pieces? _____ m and _____ m | 83 ☐

84 In a group of 36 children there are 4 more boys than girls. How many girls are there? _____ girls | 84 ☐

85 Divide a metre into 2 lengths so that one length is 9 times as long as the other. _____ cm and _____ cm | 85 ☐

Q. 86–90

Roman
numerals

Work out these sums and give your answers in Roman numerals.

86

$50 - 32 =$ _____

87

$38 + 41 =$ _____

88

$20 \times 4 =$ _____

89

$18 + 39 =$ _____

90

$3 \times 33 =$ _____

86 ☐
87 ☐
88 ☐
89 ☐
90 ☐

MARK ☐

MARK
✓ or ✗

Q. 91–95

area of
shapes

From the dimensions given, give the area of each rectangle.

91

7 cm

12 cm

_____ cm²

92

8 cm

9½ cm

_____ cm²

93

5 m

16 m

_____ m²

94

100 m

¼ km

_____ m²

95

3.4 m

7.2 m

_____ m²

91 ☐

92 ☐

93 ☐

94 ☐

95 ☐

Q. 96–100

angles
and degrees

With the clock face to help you,
write down how many degrees
the hour hand of a clock passes
through between these times.

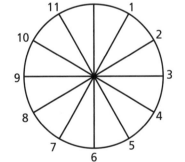

96 1 a.m. and 2 a.m.   _____ °

97 5 a.m. and 9 a.m.   _____ °

98 11 a.m. and 4.30 p.m.   _____ °

99 6 p.m. and 5 a.m.   _____ °

100 3.45 p.m. and 9.15 p.m.   _____ °

96 ☐

97 ☐

98 ☐

99 ☐

100 ☐

END OF TEST

PAPER 7 TOTAL MARK ☐

Progress chart

Write the score (out of 100) for each paper in the box provided at the bottom of the chart. Then colour in the column above the box to the appropriate height to represent this score.

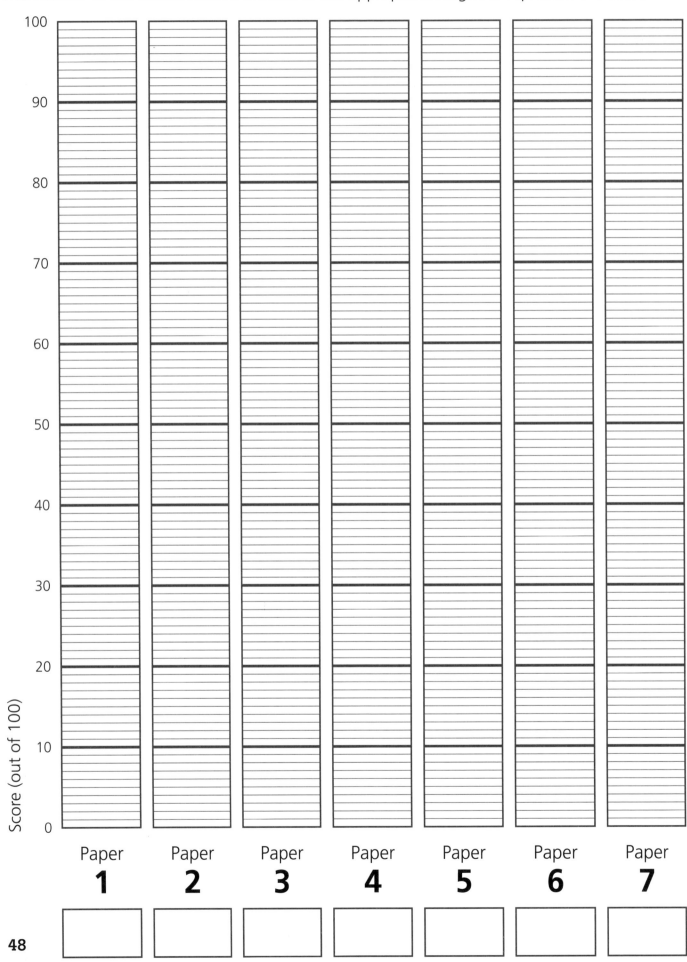

Score (out of 100)

Paper **1** Paper **2** Paper **3** Paper **4** Paper **5** Paper **6** Paper **7**

48